FOLENS
One-a-Week

Math Tests AGE '11

Folens
Publishers

Concepts tested

Concepts	Tests
Number sequences	1-4, 8-10, 13-17, 19-25, 27-28, 30-40
Odd/even	1, 6, 11, 12, 15-18, 20, 21, 27, 31, 32, 35
Prime numbers	11, 12, 18, 21-23, 27, 34, 35, 37
Factors	2-4, 10, 11, 18, 21-23, 27, 34, 35, 37
Prime factors	24-26, 31, 33, 36
Highest common factor (HCF)	19, 26, 30, 31, 33-37
Square numbers	9, 10, 13-16, 18-25, 28-30, 33, 34, 38, 40
Rectangular numbers	7, 8
Triangular numbers	2-4, 6, 8, 11, 12
Cube numbers	13, 18
Numbers to the power of 4, 5, 6, etc.	32-40
Multiples	19-21, 24
Lowest common multiple (LCM)	19, 26, 30, 31, 33-37
Percentages	17-20, 22, 23, 25, 28-30, 32, 33, 38
Ratio	6-8, 10-14, 16, 22, 34, 36, 37, 39
Addition	6, 8-17, 19-25, 27, 31, 34-40
Subtraction	1-7, 10, 12, 14, 16, 19-21, 26, 28-30, 36, 37, 39, 40
Multiplication	5, 6, 8, 11, 13, 15, 17-19, 21-24, 26-28, 32, 34, 35, 37, 38, 40
Product	2, 35, 39
Division	1, 2, 5, 7-11, 13-20, 22, 23, 25-31, 33, 38-40
Place value	6, 8-11, 13, 16, 19-22, 24, 26, 31-34, 38-40
Fractions	1-13, 15-25, 28-36, 38, 39
Decimals	1-3, 5-10, 12-19, 22-26, 31, 32, 34, 38, 40
Magic squares	3, 5, 17, 19, 22, 23, 27, 31, 36, 38-40
Algebra	6, 7, 9, 11, 16, 18, 20, 21, 26, 29, 30, 34, 38
Brackets	5, 15, 16, 19, 21, 22, 25, 27, 34, 40
Averages	1-6, 9, 10, 15, 17, 20, 32, 33, 35
Logic	1, 3-13, 15-17, 20, 21, 23, 25-30, 32-40
Time	1-3, 6, 8-14, 17-19, 24, 28, 30-39
Calendar	1, 3-8, 10, 11, 13, 14, 16, 21, 22, 38
Plane shapes	1, 3-8, 10, 11, 13, 14, 16, 21, 22, 38
Solid shapes	1, 7, 10, 11, 17-21, 24, 25, 28-30, 32-34, 36-40
Symmetry	13, 15, 38
Parallel/perpendicular/horizontal/vertical	2, 6, 9, 26, 29, 30
Angles	1, 2, 4, 5, 7-11, 14-16, 18, 22-25, 27-40

Introduction

One-a-Week Maths Tests have been designed to address the needs of busy teachers. They have been compiled to provide instant tests to help the teacher to assess children's understanding of the basic rules of number.

The tests become progressively more challenging towards the end of the book, allowing the teacher to select appropriate tests for individual children. However, each test contains an element of revision, providing some questions of a similar level to the preceding tests.

The grid on page 2 shows the content and level of each test.

The early tests may require some input from the teacher until the children are used to the format. The consistent presentation and use of language should soon become familiar to the children, helping reluctant readers to focus on the mathematical rather than the reading challenge of each question.

Recording

At the end of each test is a space for the children or teacher to record the number of correct answers.

'How well did I do?' on page 4 consists of a graph on which the children can record their test marks. They, or the teacher, will need to enter on the horizontal axis the numbers of the tests to be attempted. A block of ten tests may be recorded on each copy of the graph. This not only involves the children in monitoring their own progress, but also gives practice in handling data for a purpose and using mathematics in everyday situations.

The graphs provide the teacher with a simple visual record of how each child is meeting the demands of the tests.

The tests, answers and recording graphs may be photocopied for use within the purchasing institution.

Answers

Answers for the tests appear on pages 45–48. They are presented in a format that matches the answer strips on the pupil pages, facilitating easy checking by the teacher or child.

Test 1

1.	$\frac{7}{10}$
2.	5
3.	no
4.	150
5.	150
6.	d
7.	1000
8.	168 hours
9.	0.01
10.	75
11.	18
12.	6
13.	d
14.	5
15.	13

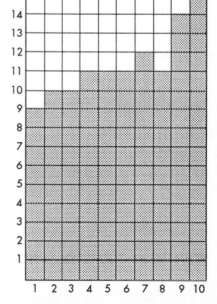

How well did I do?

How well did I do?

Shade in your test scores on this graph.

Test score

15
14
13
12
11
10
9
8
7
6
5
4
3
2
1

Test numbers

Test 1

1.

Write 0.7 as a fraction.

2.

How many sides has a pentagon?

3.

Is this true?
5 – 3 – 1 = 5 – (3 – 1)

4.

Find the sum of the even numbers between 47 and 53.

5.

I can type 25 envelopes in 10 minutes. How many can I type in one hour?

6. Which is a right angle?

a   b   c

d

7. Packets of tea are packed in cartons of 10. A pallet holds 100 cartons.

How many packets does a pallet hold?

8.

How many hours in a week?

9.

Write $\frac{1}{100}$ as a decimal.

10.

$60 \div 4 = \underline{} \div 5$

11.

Find the average of 21, 17 and 16.

12. When you multiply a number by 7 and add 8 to the answer, you get 50. What is the number?

13. Which is an acute angle?

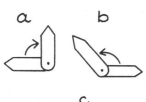

a   b

c   d

14.

120 words fit on a page. How many pages would I need to write a short story of 600 words?

15. What is the next number?

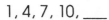 1, 4, 7, 10, ___

Answers:
1.
2.
3.
4.
5.
6.
7.
8.
9.
10.
11.
12.
13.
14.
15.

Test 2

Answers

1.
How many months have 31 days?

2. What is the sum of the numbers here that are divisible by 5.

70, 164, 430, 525

3. What is the average of 3.5, 5.0 and 0.5?

4. What is the next number?

1, 11, 21, ___

5. The ceiling and the floor in this room are _____ (vertical, perpendicular, horizontal).

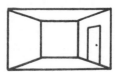

6. The 4th triangular number is 10.
Write down the 5th triangular number.

1st ○ (1)
2nd (3)
3rd (6)
4th (10)

7. Which number in this set is not a factor of 48?

{1, 2, 3, 4, 5, 6, 8, 12, 16, 24, 48}

8. Change 243 hours to days and hours.

9. Subtract $\frac{1}{2}$ from 1.25.

10. Take five hundredths from 1.72.

11. What is the highest number that is a factor of 36 and 48?

12. What is the next number?

72, 60, 48, ___

13. Which are obtuse angles?

14. Which is an acute angle?

a   b   c   d

15.
Add the sum of 7 and 8 to the product of 7 and 8.

Answers

1.

2.

3.

4.

5.

6.

7.

8.

9.

10.

11.

12.

13.

14.

15.

Test 3

1. Write all the factors of 20.

2. $\frac{1}{2}$ of a number is 18. What is $\frac{3}{4}$ of the same number?

3. How many seconds are there in one hour? (360, 3600, 36 000)

4. What is the next number? 1, 2, 4, 8, ___

5. What is the average of 6.5, 7.5 and 8.5?

6.

January						
Su	M	Tu	W	Th	F	Sa
	1	2	3	4	5	6
7	8	9	10	11	12	13

On what day is 23rd February?

7. When you multiply a number by 8 and subtract 15 from your answer you get 49. What is the number?

8. How many minutes in $13\frac{1}{2}$ hours?

9. Subtract $\frac{1}{4}$ from 0.3.

10. Take $\frac{3}{4}$ from 2.5

11. What is the missing number? 52, 39, ___, 13

12. What fraction of 1000 is 500?

13. What is the 6th triangular number?

1st	(1)
2nd	(3)
3rd	(6)
4th	(10)

14. This magic square adds up to 78 in each direction. What is the value of A?

24	16	
A	22	
		20

15. Isaac Newton, the famous mathematician, died in 1727 at the age of 85. In which year was he born?

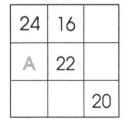

Answers:
1.
2.
3.
4.
5.
6.
7.
8.
9.
10.
11.
12.
13.
14.
15.

Test 4

1. What are the factors of 48?

2. A crate holds 12 bottles. Crates are packed in containers of 10. How many bottles are packed in 12 containers?

3. What number is half way between 17 and 31?

4. What is the next number?

0, 3, 9, 21, ___

5. Ten years is a decade. How many decades are there in a century?

6. Is this a reflex, acute or obtuse angle?

7. What date is the last day of 1996? (Write in figures).

8. Write three common factors of 16 and 24.

9. $\frac{1}{10} = \frac{}{100}$

10. Reduce ten thousand by ten.

11. Find the sum of one tenth and one hundredth.

12. What is the average of 12, 9, 14 and 13?

13. Which is the reflex angle?

14. Which is an obtuse angle?

a   b   c   d

 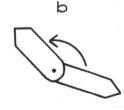  

15. The 8th triangular number is 36. What is the 7th triangular number?

Answers

1.
2.
3.
4.
5.
6.
7.
8.
9.
10.
11.
12.
13.
14.
15.

Test 5

1. Take five tenths from 2.45.	**2.** Elizabeth is not as tall as Tricia. Nancy is not as short as Tricia. Who is the tallest?

3. What is the next fraction?

$1, \frac{1}{2}, \frac{1}{4}, \frac{1}{8},$ ___

4. What is the sum of the even numbers between 51 and 57?

5. If you face north and turn clockwise to face west, how many right angles will you turn through?

6. The value of each column, row and diagonal is the same. What is the value of A?

	7	12
	10	
8	A	

7. What is the value of **B**?

B	14	24
	20	C
16		

8. What is the value of **C**?

9. $(108 \div 6) \times 6 =$ ___

10. What is the average of 18, 12, 13 and 17?

11. What fraction of this shape is shaded?

12. 1992 was a leap year. Will 2020 be a leap year?

13. You can only turn the switch in the direction of the arrow (clockwise). Through how many right angles will you turn it when you switch from **Off** to **Medium**?

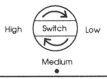

14. There are 90 degrees in a right angle. How many degrees in a straight line?

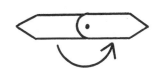

15. If 12 is subtracted from $\frac{1}{10}$ of a certain number the answer is 13. What is the number?

Answers

1.
2.
3.
4.
5.
6.
7.
8.
9.
10.
11.
12.
13.
14.
15.

Test 6

1. $2.5 + 5 + 2.05 =$ ___	2. Which letters have perpendicular lines? **A C E J H M**

3. What is the value of y?

$$y + 7 = 21 - 6$$

4. Brian is taller than Carol but smaller than Robert. Who is the smallest?

5. What is the 9th triangular number?

6. Jim's watch is 5 minutes fast. At what time (on his watch) must he start his 15-minute journey to school if he has to be there at 9.10am.

7. How many glasses of orange juice can be filled from 138 bottles, each holding 6 glasses?

8. What is the sum of the odd numbers between 14 and 20?

9. What is the value of 8 in 1.83?

10. $2 - 0.2 =$ ___

11. How many days are there from 27 May to 5 June?

12. What is the average of 16, 18, 14 and 12?

13. Ratio is a way of comparing.

The apples are in a ratio of 4 to 3 (written 4:3). In what ratio are the leaves?

14.

In what ratio are the spots on these dice?

15. The ratio of dogs to bones is ___ to ___.

Answers

1.
2.
3.
4.
5.
6.
7.
8.
9.
10.
11.
12.
13.
14.
15.

Test 7

1.
$$\frac{4}{9} = \frac{}{36}$$

2. Draw a dot pattern to show that 12 is a rectangular number.

3. What is the value of n?

4n = 100

4. Three out of every 7 children in a class are boys. What is the ratio of boys to girls?

5. Fifty chocolates were shared among 8 girls and 6 boys. If each girl got four chocolates, how many did each boy get?

6. If Michelle was twice her present age, she would be 8 years younger than her mother, who is 38. How old is Michelle?

7. How many days are there from 25 November to 7 December? (Include both days.)

8. Subtract 0.01 from 0.1

9. Take 0.05 from 1.5

10.
$$\frac{}{6} = \frac{3}{18}$$

11. How many degrees in $1\frac{1}{2}$ right angles?

12. What is the value of y in this equation?
$$3y = 19 + 5$$

13. Which is the odd one out?

a   c   d

14. Which shape is a parallelogram?

b   e

15. My grandad died in 1993. He was 78 years old. When was he born?

Answers
1.
2.
3.
4.
5.
6.
7.
8.
9.
10.
11.
12.
13.
14.
15.

Test 8

1.

$32.6 \times 10 = \underline{\ \ \ }$

2.

Three out of 8 children in a class are girls. What is the ratio of boys to girls?

3. Put in order of size, smallest first:

$8.2, 8\frac{1}{4}, 8.19$

4.

$12 \overline{\smash{)}2163}$

5.

There are 24 horses in the stables. Eight are black. The rest are brown. What is the ratio of black to brown horses?

6.

What did a dart player score if she hit 17 with her first dart, triple 15 with her second and double 9 with her third?

7. Insert a decimal point so that the 8 has a value of eight hundredths:

3768

8. Which is an acute angle? $135°, 90°, 60°, 270°$

9.

$27.50 \times 10 = \underline{\ \ \ }$

10. What is the value of 8 in 263.028?

11. Which of these numbers is both rectangular and triangular? 1, 5, 21

12. How many days are there altogether in June, July and August?

13.

'The Late Show' started at 9.20pm and finished 1hr 55min later. At what time did it finish?

14.

A game which lasted 90 minutes started at 11.30am. If the half-time break lasted twelve minutes and there were 4 minutes of injury time added on, at what time did the game end?

15.

When some stickers were shared, Mike got $\frac{2}{5}$ of them. He gave 5 to Pat and had 9 left. How many stickers were there altogether?

Answers

1.
2.
3.
4.
5.
6.
7.
8.
9.
10.
11.
12.
13.
14.
15.

Test 9

Answers

1. What must be added to 72 so that it will divide exactly into 5 groups of 16?

2. The product of three numbers is 96. Two of the numbers are 8 and 3. What is the other?

3. Put in order of size, smallest first:

   $\frac{12}{10}$, $\frac{12}{100}$, 1.1

4. What is the average of $2\frac{1}{4}$, $3\frac{1}{2}$, $1\frac{3}{4}$, and $4\frac{1}{2}$?

5. Each rung on a ladder is ___ to the side of the ladder. (parallel, vertical, perpendicular)

6. Karen's watch is four minutes fast. At what time (on her watch) must she start her 20-minute journey to school if she has to be there by 9.15am?

7. $\frac{8}{12}$ is $\frac{2}{3}$ when re-named in its lowest terms. Write $\frac{12}{18}$ in its lowest terms.

8. Which is an acute angle? 270°, 45°, 90°, 135°

9. $9\overline{\smash{)}6543}$

10. $127.75 \div 10 =$ ___

11. What is the value of n?

    $4n + 6 = 18$

12. $\frac{264}{2}$

13. A secretary is at the office from 9.30am until 5pm five days a week. How many hours a week does he work?

14. Nine is a square number.

    Which of these are square numbers: 6, 12, 16, 36?

15. Put in order of size, smallest first: 3.88, $3\frac{1}{2}$, 3.09

Answers
1.
2.
3.
4.
5.
6.
7.
8.
9.
10.
11.
12.
13.
14.
15.

Test 10

Answers

1. How many hundredths in 1.85?

2. What is the missing number?

   100, 81, 63, ___, 30, 15

3. $3.05 + 16.27 =$ ___

4. Take three thousand from 300 000.

5. Oliver practises the piano for $\frac{3}{4}$ of an hour five days a week. How long does he practise altogether in the week?

6. Which of these is a square number?

   6, 12, 28, 49, 60

7. 12 children each have a dog, 9 have a cat.

   What is the ratio of dogs to cats?

8. How many right angles in a full turn (rotation)?

9. $\frac{7}{8}$ of 10 = ___

10. $11 \overline{)7238}$

11. How many sides has an octagon?

12. What is the average of 36, 26, 30 and 28?

13. If Carol was three times her present age, she would be 3 years older than her father, who is 33. How old is Carol?

14. What is the missing number?

    100, 85, ___, 58, 46

15. What is the highest number that is a factor of both 45 and 72?

Answers
1.
2.
3.
4.
5.
6.
7.
8.
9.
10.
11.
12.
13.
14.
15.

Test 11

Answers

1.
What are the factors of 13?

2.
Rita will be 27 in 2002. How old was she in 1980?

3. What is the next number?

3, 5, 9, 15, ___

4. What fraction of a full rotation is 90°?
($\frac{1}{4}$, $\frac{1}{2}$ or $\frac{3}{4}$)

5.
19 is a prime number. A prime number has no factors except itself and ___.

6. 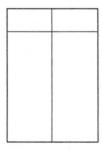 Two triangular numbers (3, 6) make the square number 9. What two triangular numbers make this square number?

7.
What must you multiply 15 by to get an answer which is half of 150?

8.
Add the even numbers between 43 and 53.

9. What is the value of 6 in 204.036?

10.
1.50 x 100 = ___

11. What is the value of y?

8y − 5 = 11

12.
2163 ÷ 100 = ___

13. How many rectangles can you see here?

14.
Three out of every five children in a class are girls. If there are 18 girls, how many boys are there?

15.
Olivia is at school from 9.30am until 3.30pm.
What fraction of the day does she spend at school?

Answers:
1.
2.
3.
4.
5.
6.
7.
8.
9.
10.
11.
12.
13.
14.
15.

Test 12

1.	
2.	

1.

$$35 - 17 = \frac{1}{2} \text{ of } \underline{\quad}$$

2. The clock hands show 5 o'clock. Through how many degrees must the minute hand turn to show a time of 5.45?

3. Is 12 a triangular number?

4. My book has 96 pages. I have read $\frac{5}{8}$ of them. How many have I still to read?

5. There are 60 flowers. The ratio of pink to white flowers is 5 : 7. How many white flowers are there?

6. If you add two odd numbers is the answer odd or even?

7. Two out of every five children in a class are boys. If there are 21 girls, how many boys are there?

8. Add the prime numbers between 4 and 12.

9. $0.01 \times 85 = \underline{\quad}$

10. $\frac{2}{9}$ of $189 = \underline{\quad}$

11. Add the odd numbers between 56 and 62.

12. Which number in this list is not a prime number?
2, 3, 5, 11, 15

13. A clock shows 1.30. Through how many degrees must the minute hand turn to show a time of 2.30?

14. Add the even numbers between 61 and 71.

15. What is the next prime number?   31, 37, 41, ___

Answers

1.
2.
3.
4.
5.
6.
7.
8.
9.
10.
11.
12.
13.
14.
15.

Test 13

1. Which is the greatest?

$\frac{1}{4}$, $\frac{3}{8}$, $\frac{1}{16}$, $\frac{5}{16}$

2. What number is ten times greater than a hundred thousand?

3. What is the value of 6 in 101.63?

4. $9^2 + 12^3 + 13^3 = $ ___

5. How many axes of symmetry has this kite?

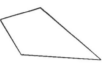

6. Which shape is symmetrical?

a   b   c

7.
4 x 4 = 16
4 squared = 16
$4^2 = 16$
What number is 5^2?

8.
$12\overline{)2623}$

9. What number is 6^2?

10. $1 + 3 + 5 + $ ___ $ = 4^2$

11. My aunt was born in 1947. When will she be 60 years old?

12. What is the next number?
1, 2, 6, 14, ___

13. Three out of every 7 of the girls in a class have bikes. If 12 girls have bikes, how many have not?

14. Clare's watch is 5 minutes slow. At what time (on her watch) must she start her ten-minute journey to the bus stop to catch the 9.05am bus?

15. What is 7 squared (7^2)?

Answers
1.
2.
3.
4.
5.
6.
7.
8.
9.
10.
11.
12.
13.
14.
15.

Test 14

1.

$$4^2 \div 2^2 = \underline{\quad}$$

2. What is the missing number?

1, 4, 9, 16, ___, 36

3. What number is 8^2?

4.

$$2.8 \div 0.4 = \underline{\quad}$$

5. What is the next prime number?

17, 19, 23, 29, ___

6.

Marie gave two fifths of her stickers to Susan but still had 18 left.

How many did she give to Susan?

7. How many axes of symmetry has this shape?

8.

$$10\,\overline{)\,2132\,}$$

9. What is the next fraction?

$1, \frac{1}{3}, \frac{1}{9}, \underline{\quad}$

10. How many degrees in $\frac{1}{4}$ of a full rotation?

11. Use +, −, x or ÷ to complete this:

$$32 \div 2 = 24 \underline{\quad} 8$$

12. Five out of every 8 girls in a class like lemonade. If 20 girls like it, how many do not?

13.

A nurse working on night shift starts at 8pm and finishes at 7.15am. How many hours does she work in a week if she works 4 nights?

14.

January						
Su	M	Tu	W	Th	F	Sa
	1	2	3	4	5	6
7	8	9	10	11	12	13

On what day was 14th December?

15. What is the next number?

0.25, 0.5, 0.75, 1.0, ___

Answers

1.
2.
3.
4.
5.
6.
7.
8.
9.
10.
11.
12.
13.
14.
15.

Test 15

1.

What is 9^2?

2.

What fraction of a full rotation is 60˚?

3.

$12 \overline{)6130}$

4.

What is the average of 0.3, 3 and 30?

5.

Buses leave the bus depot every 10 minutes from 6.30am. At what time will the 4th bus leave?

6.

Seventy-two chocolates were shared among 14 boys and 15 girls. If each boy received 3 chocolates, how many did each girl get?

7.

$(12 \times 7) + (12 \times 3)$

$= 12 \times \underline{\quad}$

8.

What is the average of 2.4 and 3.2?

9.

$0.4 \times 15 = \underline{\quad}$

10.

What fraction of 6 is $1\frac{1}{2}$?

11.

$8^2 = 52 + \underline{\quad}$

12.

What is the missing number?
24, 22, 18, ___, 4

13. What two triangular numbers make this square number?

• • • • •
• • • • •
• • • • •
• • • • •
• • • • •

14. Martin is facing north. If he turns right (clockwise) through two right angles, in what direction will he be facing?

N
W —— E
S

15.

What is the sum of the even numbers between 97 and 103?

Answers

1.
2.
3.
4.
5.
6.
7.
8.
9.
10.
11.
12.
13.
14.
15.

Test 16

Answers

1. The year 2010 will be in which century?

2. The ratio of men to women in a club is 3 : 7. There are 50 members of the club. How many are men?

3.
$$12\,\overline{)3126}$$

4. What is the next fraction?

$1, \frac{1}{10}, \frac{1}{100}, \frac{1}{1000}, \_\_\_$

5. What is the next number?

16, 25, 36, 49, 64, ___

6. How many seats are there in a hall that has 30 rows of 15 seats each side of the centre aisle?

7. Angela was 12 years and 4 months old in December 1994. In which year and month was she born?

8. What is the value of m?
$7m - 10 = 39$

9. $0.04 \times 125 = \_\_\_$

10. $26 \div (3^2 + 2^2) = \_\_\_$

11. Which is the greatest?

6.13, 31.6, 131.6

12. What is 12^2?

13. Dan is facing east. If he turned clockwise through 3 right angles, in what direction would he be facing?

N
W —— E
S

14. The middle number of seven consecutive even numbers is 1004. What is the first number?

15. What is the sum of the odd numbers between 98 and 106?

Answers

1.
2.
3.
4.
5.
6.
7.
8.
9.
10.
11.
12.
13.
14.
15.

Test 17

1.	2. What are the
Write 1% as a decimal.	values of A and B?

50	100	30
40		
90	A	B

3.	4. What is the next fraction?
Write 1% as a fraction.	$\frac{5}{1}$, $\frac{10}{2}$, $\frac{15}{3}$, ___

5.

A _____ divides a circle into two halves.
(circumference, radius, diameter)

6. A theatre has 29 rows of 13 seats on one side and 28 rows of 14 seats on the other side.

How many seats are there altogether?

7. Share 60 apples between 2 people in the ratio 9 : 11.

How many apples will each person have?

8.

$11\overline{)3941}$

9.	10.
0.8 of 12 = ___	$\frac{7}{12}$ + $\frac{19}{24}$ = ___

11.	12.
What is the sum of the first ten odd numbers?	186 x 13 = ___

13. A game that lasted 80 minutes started at 2.15pm. The half-time break lasted 8 minutes and there were 7 minutes added on for stoppages.
At what time did the game finish?

14. What are the values of A and B?

12	8	A
	11	
B		10

15.

What is the average of 23, 24 and 25?

Answers

1.

2.

3.

4.

5.

6.

7.

8.

9.

10.

11.

12.

13.

14.

15.

Test 18

1. Write $\frac{1}{4}$ as a decimal.

2. A watch is 8 minutes slow and shows 9:15. Another is 8 minutes fast. What does the second watch show?

3. $13^2 = $ ___

4. What is the highest factor of 27, not counting 27?

5. What fraction of this shape is shaded?

6. Pat is facing south. If he turns anti-clockwise (left) through an angle of 270°, in what direction will he be facing?

N
W —|— E
S

7. A multiple of 3 is any number that has 3 as a factor. Which is not a multiple of 3?
3, 12, 36, 48, 81, 109

8. $13\overline{)7601}$

9. $10^3 = $ ___

10. Write $\frac{1}{4}$ as a percentage.

11. The only even number which is also a prime number is ___.

12. $a = 8$ $b = 4$

$a^2 \div b^2 = $ ___

13. 3 is a factor of 6.

3 is also a factor of 9.

3 is a common factor of 6 and 9.

What is a common factor of 15 and 25?

14. The diameter of a circle is twice the length of the _____.

(circumference, width, radius)

15. Oliver sleeps from 10pm until 8am. What fraction of a day does he spend in bed?

Answers
1.
2.
3.
4.
5.
6.
7.
8.
9.
10.
11.
12.
13.
14.
15.

Test 19

1. What is 5% of 100?	2. What is the highest common factor (h.c.f) of 24 and 32?
3. What is the difference between 3^2 and 2^3?	4. Which are multiples of 7? 38, 57, 63, 67, 84

5. What is the missing square number?

81, 100, ___, 144

6. Which of these regular polygons is a pentagon?	7. Insert a decimal point so that the 8 has a value of eight thousandths: 3768
	8. $2^2 + 12^2 =$ ___

9. $(29 \times 7) + (29 \times 3) =$ ___	10. Write $\frac{7}{1000}$ as a decimal.
11. Write $\frac{3}{4}$ as a percentage.	12. $14\overline{)2061}$
13. What are the values of A and B?	14. Put in order, smallest first: 2.39, 2.048, 2.04.

13.

18		A
		B
15	20	16

15. This is a clock face in a mirror. What is the time in figures?

Answers
1.
2.
3.
4.
5.
6.
7.
8.
9.
10.
11.
12.
13.
14.
15.

Test 20

1.

$$10^2 - 10^1 = \underline{\quad}$$

2. If you subtract an odd number from an odd number, is the answer an odd number or an even number?

3. What is the value of y?

$$\frac{y}{4} = 5$$

4. Is this true?

$$0.099 > 0.1$$

5. 25% of the children walk to school, 17% cycle, 30% come by bus and the rest travel by car.
What percentage travel by car?

6. A newsagent sells 60 newspapers on a Sunday and an average of 25 newspapers each of the other weekdays. What is her daily average for the whole week?

7. What is the missing square number?

169, 196, ___, 256

8.

$$14\overline{\smash{)}1721}$$

9.

$$10^3 - 10^2 = \underline{\quad}$$

10.

$$\frac{1}{10} = \underline{\quad}\%$$

11. Put in order, smallest first:
2.2, 2.22, 2.199

12.

$$14^2 + 12^2 = \underline{\quad}$$

13. Which of these triangles is a regular polygon?

a   b

c   d

14. Twelve is a multiple of 3. It is also a multiple of 4. Which of these numbers are multiples of both 4 and 6?

16, 20, 24, 30, 36

15. What is 10% of 250?

Answers

1.

2.

3.

4.

5.

6.

7.

8.

9.

10.

11.

12.

13.

14.

15.

One–a–Week Maths Tests: Age 10–11

Test 21

1. What is the next number?
100, 10, 1, ___

2. Simon swapped $\frac{2}{5}$ of his 40 marbles for 9 of Saqib's. How many has Simon got now?

3. What is the sum of the odd numbers between 48 and 54?

4. Which of these are common multiples of 3 and 6?
9, 12, 15, 18, 21

5. In a class of 40, 90% of the children got an answer right. How many children got the answer wrong?

6.

April						
Su	M	Tu	W	Th	F	Sa
			1	2	3	4
5	6	7	8	9	10	11

On what day is 26th June?

7. 3 x 3 x 3 is the same as 3 cubed (3^3).
$3^3 = 27$

What is 4^3?

8. $3^2 + 7^2 + 16^2 =$ ___

9. $\frac{9}{10} =$ ___ %

10. $(9 \times 6) - (12 \times 4) =$ ___

11. Put in order, smallest first:
1.19, 1.019, 1.02

12. What is the next number?

8, 4, 2, 1, ___

13. What is the sum of the first 3 prime numbers?
(1 is not counted as a prime number)

14. Which shape is not a regular polygon:
a square, a rectangle, an equilateral triangle?

15. m= 4, n = 7

2m – n = ___

Answers

1.

2.

3.

4.

5.

6.

7.

8.

9.

10.

11.

12.

13.

14.

15.

Test 22

1.	3% of 150 = ___
2.	A box contains pens and pencils in the ratio 6 : 5. There are 24 pens. How many pencils are there?

1.

2.

3.
$$7^3 = \text{___}$$

4. What is the next number?

0.2, 2, 20, ___

3.

4.

5. Angles that meet on a straight line always add up to 180°. What is the size of angle A?

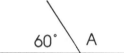

60° A

5.

6.

6. What are the values of A and B?

33	A	B
12	27	
36		21

7.

Are prime numbers rectangular in shape?

8.
$$16^2 + 8^2 = \text{___}$$

7.

8.

9.

9.
$$72 = 2 \times \text{___} \times 3$$

10.
8% of 25 = ___

10.

11.

11. What angle is shown at A?

30°
A

12.
$$\frac{1.4}{0.7} = \text{___}$$

12.

13.

13.

What is the next number?

(Clue: $2^3 = 8$)

8, 27, 64, ___

14.

The date is Tuesday 26th January.

On what day will 27th February be?

14.

15.

15.
$$(8 \times 5) + (24 \times 6) = \text{___}$$

One-a-Week Maths Tests: Age 10–11

Test 23

1.

$\frac{1}{4}$ = ___ %

2.

$2^3 + 6^2 + 3^3$ = ___

3.

999 x 9 = ___

4.

___ x 3^2 = 18

5.

What is the size of angle A?

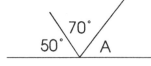

70°
50° A

6.

A prime factor is a factor that is a prime number. The prime factors of 12 are 2 x 2 x 3 or 2^2 x 3.

The prime factors of 24 are 2^3 x ___.

7.

$8^3 - 4^3$ = ___

8. 5% of 200 cyclists gave up before the end of a race. How many finished?

9.

689 x 1000 = ___

10.

$\frac{1.4}{0.07}$ = ___

11.

What is the next number?
400, 40, 4, ___

12.

25% of 500 = ___

13.

Francis did three English exams. He got 50% of the marks in the first exam, 46% in the second and 51% in the third. What was his average percentage mark in English?

14. What are the values of A and B?

12		A
12	11	10
B	14	

15.

25% of a class do not play basketball. 27 children do play. How many children are in the class?

Answers

1.

2.

3.

4.

5.

6.

7.

8.

9.

10.

11.

12.

13.

14.

15.

Test 24

1.

$$16^3 + 4^3 = \underline{\hspace{1cm}}$$

2. Put in order of size, smallest first.

1.009, 1.011, 1.01

3. The prime factors of 20 are

$\underline{\hspace{0.8cm}}^2$ and 5.

4. Write 75% as a fraction in its lowest terms.

5. What is the size of angle A?

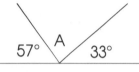

57°   A   33°

6. Which of these is a multiple of 2?

15, 23, 26, 31

7. Which fraction is greater than $\frac{1}{4}$ but less than $\frac{1}{2}$?

$\frac{1}{8}$, $\frac{1}{3}$, $\frac{7}{10}$, $\frac{9}{10}$

8. How many thousands are in $\frac{1}{2}$ a million?

9.

$$100 \times 100 = \underline{\hspace{1cm}}$$

10. What is the size of angle B?

B   45°   90°

11. What fraction of 1 hour is 24 minutes (in its lowest terms)?

12.

$$6^2 + 11^2 = \underline{\hspace{1cm}}$$

13. The angles of a triangle add up to 180°.

What is the size of angle B?

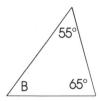

55°   B   65°

14. Angles that meet to make a complete revolution add up to 360°.

What is the size of angle A?

300°   A

15. Which of these are common multiples of 4 and 7?

12, 14, 16, 28. 32, 56

Answers

1.

2.

3.

4.

5.

6.

7.

8.

9.

10.

11.

12.

13.

14.

15.

Test 25

1. What is the next number?

30, 3, 0.3, ___

2. Two angles of a triangle are 30 degrees and 80 degrees. What is the size of the third angle?

3. $(150 \times 2) + (41 \times 2) =$ ___

4. Write 20% as a fraction, in its lowest terms.

5. What was a dart player's score if she scored double 19 with her first dart, 9 with her second and triple 16 with her third?

6. One winter's day the temperature was 2° Celsius. That night it dropped to –2°C. How many degrees colder was the night?

7. The prime factors of 48 are 2^4 and ___.

8. $(4 + 3)^2 - (2^2 + 3^2) =$ ___

9. $2^4 \times 5 =$ ___

10. $15\overline{)2198}$

11. When $\frac{3}{5}$ of a certain number is reduced by 9 the result is 21. What is the number?

12. Which of these are common multiples of 6 and 8?
12, 16, 24, 32, 48

13. Which is an equilateral triangle?

a b c d

14. The temperature was –1°C during the night. The next day it rose to 6°C. How many degrees warmer was it then?

15. What is the lowest common multiple of 6, 10 and 12?

Answers
1.
2.
3.
4.
5.
6.
7.
8.
9.
10.
11.
12.
13.
14.
15.

Test 26

1. Take one hundred thousand from half a million.	2. What is the highest common factor of 27, 39 and 45?

1.

2.

3.
$$a = 4, b = 5$$
$$a^2 - 2b = \underline{\quad}$$

4. The prime factors of a number are 3^3 and 2. What is the number?

3.

4.

5. Which is the common multiple of 8, 9 and 12?

32, 96, 108, 216, 238

5.

6.

6. There are 20 rows of 16 seats on each side of the cinema.

How many seats are there altogether?

7.
$$16\overline{)2983}$$

7.

8. The temperature is 5˚C. What will the temperature be if it drops by 10˚C?

8.

9.
$$x = 5, y = 8$$
$$x^2 - 3y = \underline{\quad}$$

10.
$$1 \div \underline{\quad} = 0.01$$

9.

10.

11.
$$13^3 = \underline{\quad}$$

12. Which of these letters have parallel lines?
A E H K M Y Z

11.

12.

13. The middle number of 5 consecutive even numbers is 32. What is the first number?

32

14. In a plantation there are 14 Scots pines, twice as many Norway spruces and seven times as many Sitka spruces.

How many trees are there in the plantation?

13.

14.

15. What is the lowest common multiple (l.c.m.) of 6, 8 and 10?

15.

Test 27

1. $7^3 + 6^3 = $ ___	**2.** What is the smallest number of flowers that can be arranged in bunches of either 4, 6 or 9?
3. What is the missing number? 18, 20, 24, ___, 38	**4.** What is 75% of 350?

5. What is the highest factor of 48?

6. What is the size of angle A?  40° A	**7.** In a class the ratio of girls to boys is 4 : 5. There are 36 children altogether. How many girls are there?
	8. What is the 20th even number?
9. What is the 26th even number?	**10.** $(0 \times 9) \div 9 = $ ___
11. $16\overline{)9831}$	**12.** What is the lowest common multiple of 6 and 8?
13. A shopkeeper mixed 160 red balloons with 80 yellow balloons to make packets which have 8 balloons each. How many packets can he make?	**14.** What is the value of A?

	A	
18		14
13	20	15

15. What is the missing prime number?

37, 41, ___, 47

Answers

1.
2.
3.
4.
5.
6.
7.
8.
9.
10.
11.
12.
13.
14.
15.

Test 28

1. 40% of 65 = ___	**2.** The middle number of 5 consectuive odd numbers is 297. What is the last number?

3. What number when divided by 10 gives an answer of 10?	**4.** The temperature is –3°C. What will it be if it rises by 5°C?

5. What shape is this?

6. This shape is a quadrilateral (a four-sided shape). Its angles add up to 360°. What is the size of angle B?

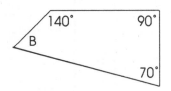

7. Andrea is $1\frac{1}{2}$ times older than her brother, Sean. If Andrea is 9, how old is Sean?

8. Write 7 marks out of 10 as a percentage.

9. $100 - 36 = 16 \times$ ___

10. What is the next number?
4.0, 3.9, 3.7, 3.4, ___

11. $18^2 =$ ___

12. What is the largest remainder you can have when you divide by 25?

13. What percentage of electricity is generated by water power?

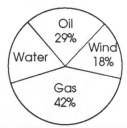

14. There were 12 minutes of advertising during a 1 hour programme. What fraction of the hour was this, in its lowest terms?

15. Which is the odd one out?

a b c d

Answers

1.
2.
3.
4.
5.
6.
7.
8.
9.
10.
11.
12.
13.
14.
15.

One-a-Week Maths Tests: Age 10–11

Test 29

1.

Reduce 900 by 10%.

2. What is angle A?

A ╱45°

3. a = 3, b = 4, c = 5
What is the value of
a + 2b + c?

4.
Toni got 40 marks out of 50.
What percentage did she
get?

5.
What is the lowest common multiple (l.c.m.) of 4, 9 and 12?

6. What is the size of angle
A?

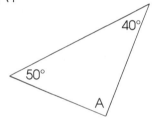

7. What is the missing
number?

$$18\overline{)}\ \ \overset{5\qquad r10}{?}$$

8.
$$21\overline{)8265}$$

9.
$21^2 =$ ___

10.
$12^3 =$ ___

11.
What is $\frac{1}{2}$ of $\frac{1}{16}$?

12. A bus holds 39 passengers.
How many buses will 420
people need?

13. What is the size of
angle B?

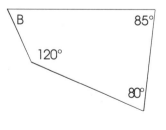

14.
What is the highest
common factor of 72,
84 and 96?

15.
Is this shape a pentagon
or a hexagon?

Answers

1.
2.
3.
4.
5.
6.
7.
8.
9.
10.
11.
12.
13.
14.
15.

Test 30

1. What is $\frac{1}{2}$ of $\frac{3}{4}$?

2. Eighteen children in a school wear glasses, 90% do not. How many children attend the school?

3. Which whole numbers are greater than –10 but less than –5?

4. Which two consecutive **square** numbers have a difference of 13?

5. What is angle A?

6. How many horizontal lines can you see on this signpost?

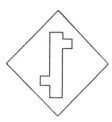

7. Peter has 114 chestnuts. If he keeps 50 for himself and shares the rest equally among his four friends, how many does each friend get?

8. What is the next number?
1, 4, 2, 8, 3, 12, ___

9. What is the l.c.m. of 8, 9 and 12?

10. $a = 3, b = 4, c = 5$
$3a + b - 2c =$ ___

11. A clock loses 10 seconds every hour. How many minutes does it lose in a day?

12.
$$20\overline{)2619}$$

13. Which is an isosceles triangle?

 a   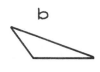 b   c

 d

14. What is angle A?

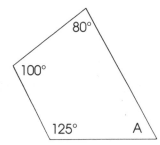

15. What is the highest common factor of 33, 66, 88 and 132?

1.
2.
3.
4.
5.
6.
7.
8.
9.
10.
11.
12.
13.
14.
15.

One-a-Week Maths Tests: Age 10–11   © Folens

Test 31

1.

$$19\overline{)7601}$$

2. What is the highest common factor (h.c.f.) of 49, 84 and 98?

3. $16^3 + 15^3 = \underline{\quad}$

4. Write in order, starting with the smallest:
−5, 0, 4, −11

5. What is the lowest common multiple (l.c.m.) of 6, 9 and 12?

6. Angles that meet to make a complete revolution add up to 360°. What is the size of angle A?

7. What is the size of angle A?

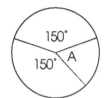

8. Put in order, starting with the smallest: $\frac{1}{10}$, 11%, $\frac{9}{100}$

9. What is the 10th odd number?

10. $\frac{1}{5} + \frac{1}{10} + \frac{1}{20} = \underline{\quad}$

11. The prime factors of a number are 2^4 and 5. What is the number?

12. $297 \div 11 = \underline{\quad}$

13. What are the values of A and B?

A		26
	20	
14	B	22

14. What fraction of this circle is shaded?

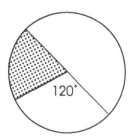

15. This is a clock in a mirror. What is the time?

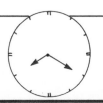

Answers
1.
2.
3.
4.
5.
6.
7.
8.
9.
10.
11.
12.
13.
14.
15.

Test 32

1. Is a sphere a prism?

2. 3^4 means $3 \times 3 \times 3 \times 3$

$3^4 =$ ___

3. What is the next number?

1250, 125, 12.5, ___

4. $1 \div 0.25 =$ ___ ($\frac{1}{4}$, 4 or 25)

5. Sixteen children in a school are left-handed. 92% are not. How many children attend the school?

6. What is the size of angle A in this equilateral triangle?

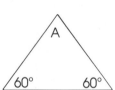

7. What is the l.c.m. of 8, 9 and 10?

8. $16\overline{)8932}$

9. What is the 20th odd number?

10. $\frac{1}{25} \times 4 =$ ___

11. 1pm on a 24-hour clock is 13:00. What is 8pm?

12. What is the next number?

1.825, 18.25, 182.5, ___

13. What fraction of this circle is shaded? ($\frac{1}{10}$, $\frac{1}{12}$ or $\frac{1}{15}$)

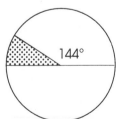

14. How many angles has a hexagon?

15. The average age of 3 girls is 16. One girl is 18, another is 13. How old is the third girl?

Answers

1.
2.
3.
4.
5.
6.
7.
8.
9.
10.
11.
12.
13.
14.
15.

Test 33

1. Write 3.15pm as on a 24-hour clock.

2. William got 150 out of 200. What percentage of the total marks was that?

3. What number is halfway between −4 and +6?

4. 3^2 is a prime factor of 63. What is the other prime factor?

5. The average age of three youths is 17. One youth is 19, another is 13. What age is the third youth?

6. What is the size of angle A in this triangle?

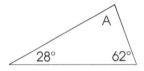

7. What is the smallest number which can be divided evenly by 500, 600 or 1000?

8. What is the next number? 1, 4, 9, 16, 25, ___

9. 23 $\overline{\smash{)}2098}$

10. $6^4 =$ ___

11. Write 23:08 using am or pm.

12. What fraction of an hour is 20 minutes? Write it in its lowest terms.

13. The average age of four women is 25. If the average age of three of them is 24, what is the age of the other woman?

14. What is the size of angle X?

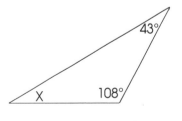

15. What is the h.c.f. of 13, 39 and 78?

	Answers
1.	
2.	
3.	
4.	
5.	
6.	
7.	
8.	
9.	
10.	
11.	
12.	
13.	
14.	
15.	

Test 34

1.

$28 \times 29 = \underline{\ \ \ }$.

2. The middle person in a row is the 16th. How many people are in the row?

3.

$8^4 = \underline{\ \ \ }$

4. What is the next number?

0.005, 0.05, 0.5, ___

5.

$(12^2 + 3^2) \times 4^3 = \underline{\ \ \ }$

6. Biscuits are shared in the ratio 2 : 1. If the larger share is 30, what is the smaller share?

7. Anthony ran a lap in 30.00 seconds. Christopher ran it in 29.05 seconds. How much faster was Christopher?

8. What is this shape?

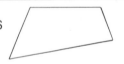

9.

$9^4 = \underline{\ \ \ }$

10. What is the next fraction?

$1\frac{1}{2}, 2\frac{3}{4}, 4, 5\frac{1}{4}, \underline{\ \ \ }$

11. $a = 4, b = 7, c = 5$

$\dfrac{b + c}{a} = \underline{\ \ \ }$

12. What is the h.c.f. of 36, 54 and 72?

13. A theatre has 4 seats in each of 2 boxes, 13 rows of 20 seats in each side of the stalls and 15 rows of 19 seats in the circle. How many seats are there altogether?

14. What is the size of angle A?

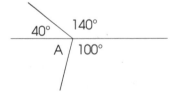

15.

Add the prime numbers between 48 and 60.

Answers

1.

2.

3.

4.

5.

6.

7.

8.

9.

10.

11.

12.

13.

14.

15.

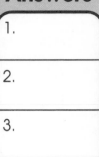

Test 35

1. Add the prime numbers between 56 and 70.

2. $2^5 = 2 \times 2 \times 2 \times 2 \times 2$

$2^5 = \underline{\quad}$

3. $\frac{1}{2} + \frac{1}{3} = \underline{\quad}$

4. What number is halfway between –8 and +4?

5. What is the product of the even numbers between 23 and 27?

6. What is the size of angle A? (70˚, 80˚ or 90˚)

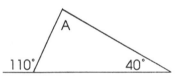

A

110˚   40˚

7. The average age of four men is 26. If the average age of three of the men is 25, what is the age of the other man?

8. Write 1 minute after midnight as on a 24-hour clock.

9. $3^5 = \underline{\quad}$

10. What is the h.c.f of 64, 72 and 96?

11. What is the missing number?
–4, ___, 0, 2, 4

12. What is the l.c.m. of 7, 8 and 14?

13. $15 \times \underline{\quad} \times 3 = 450$

14. What is the size of angle A?

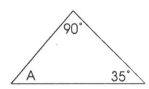

90˚

A   35˚

15. The light in the lighthouse flashes every 10 seconds. How many times does it flash in one hour?

Answers

1.

2.

3.

4.

5.

6.

7.

8.

9.

10.

11.

12.

13.

14.

15.

Test 36

1. What is the highest common factor of 36, 48 and 72?

2. 2^3 is a prime factor of 40. What is the other prime factor?

3. Write 1 minute before midnight as on a 24-hour clock.

4. What is the size of angle A?

5. The correct answer to a mathematics question was 10.5. Ruth had 1.05. By how much was her answer too small?

6. What is the size of angle A?

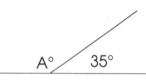

A°   35°

7. $3^3 + 6^4 + 14^2 =$ ___

8. What is the next number?
4, 2, 1, $\frac{1}{2}$, $\frac{1}{4}$, ___

9. What are the next numbers?
2, 3, 4, 6, 6, 9, ___, ___

10. $2 : 4 = 1 : 2$

$3 : 9 = 1 :$ ___

11. How many games altogether will four teams play if every team plays each other once?

12. $4^5 =$ ___

13. Which is the odd one out?

a   b   c   d

14. The rows in this magic square add up to 45 in each direction. What is the value of A?

	A	
20	15	
		14

15. x = 1, y = 6
What is the value of $y^2 \div 4x$?

Answers
1.
2.
3.
4.
5.
6.
7.
8.
9.
10.
11.
12.
13.
14.
15.

Test 37

1. Add the prime numbers between 85 and 95.

2. What is the size of angle A?

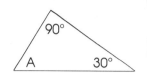

3. $3^4 + 2^5 + 1^5 =$ ___

4. Write 9.28am as on a 24-hour clock.

5. What is the l.c.m. of 2, 4, 7 and 8?

6. $2^6 = 2 \times 2 \times 2 \times 2 \times 2 \times 2$

$2^6 =$ ___

7. What is the h.c.f. of 24, 36, 40 and 52?

8. Which is the odd one out?

   a sphere, a cone, a circle, a cylinder

9. How many degrees in 5 right angles?

10. What is the next number?
    6, 4, 2, 0, ___

11. Write 11.36pm as on a 24-hour clock.

12. What two numbers are these?
    Their sum is 40.
    Their difference is 4.

13. What is the size of angle A?

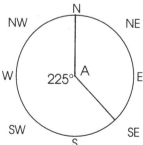

14. If you turn a complete circle, you turn through 360°.

    Through how many degrees do you turn in one eighth of a circle?

15. Rows of seats in a hall are lettered from A to Z. There are 20 seats in each row. How many seats are there altogether?

Answers

1.

2.

3.

4.

5.

6.

7.

8.

9.

10.

11.

12.

13.

14.

15.

Test 38

1.

$3^6 =$ ___

2. When you square a certain number and add 4 to it you get 40. What is the number?

3. What is the next number?

1, 3, 7, 13, ___

4. How many edges has a cuboid? (6, 8 or 12)

5. A woman is 30 years old. Her daughter is one quarter her age. What age in years and months is her daughter?

6. What is the acute angle made by the hands of this clock?

7. $\frac{3}{5}$ of the children in a class are girls. 16 are boys. How many children are there altogether?

8.

$1^6 + 2^4 + 3^2 =$ ___

9. $0.35 \times 10 \times 10 \times 10 =$ ___

10. $\frac{n}{3} = 8$ What is the value of n?

11.

$22\overline{\smash)7019}$

12. 95% of 40 children passed a test. How many did not pass?

13. How many axes of symmetry has this hexagon?

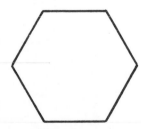

14. The rows of this magic square add up to 2.4 in each direction. What is the value of A?

27		30
	27	24
24	A	

15. There are 5 teams: red, blue, green, yellow and purple. How many games are there, if every team plays each other once?

Answers

1.
2.
3.
4.
5.
6.
7.
8.
9.
10.
11.
12.
13.
14.
15.

One-a-Week Maths Tests: Age 10–11

Test 39

1. What is the next number? 1, 5, 2, 6, 3, 7, ___	2. Add the sum of 10 and 11 to the product of 10 and 11 and the difference between 10 and 11.
3. Write twenty to five in the afternoon as on a 24-hour clock.	4. Write the ratio 20 : 30 in its lowest terms.

5. What is the obtuse angle made by the hands of this clock?	

6. What is the value of A?	7. Gold melts at 1063°C and boils at 2660°C. What is the temperature difference?

1.3	0.2	1.2
0.8		
	A	0.5

	8. Write midnight as on a 24-hour clock.
9. What is the next number? 0.001, 0.01, 0.1, ___	10. $2^7 =$ ___
11. How much short of a million is 875 000?	12. $\frac{3}{4} y = 9$ What is the value of y?
13. How many angles has a decagon? 	14. How many degrees is the clockwise turn from south east to west? 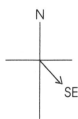

15. What is the lowest number that 3, 5 and 6 will all divide into, without leaving a remainder?

Answers

1.

2.

3.

4.

5.

6.

7.

8.

9.

10.

11.

12.

13.

14.

15.

Test 40

1.

___ ÷ 100 = 0.1

(1, 10 or 100)

2. The sum of two numbers is 80. Their difference is 8. What are the numbers?

3. What is the next number?

–5, –3, –1, ___

4. What number is 12 less than 9?

5. A watch was put right at the 8pm time signal. It lost 2 minutes every hour. What time did it show at the 8pm time signal the next day?

6. What is the size of angle A?

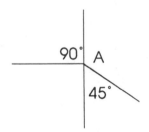

7. What is the size of angle A?

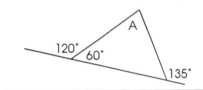

8.

$2^8 =$ ___

9.

10 – (4 x 1.95) = ___

10.

___^{2} – 11 = 70

11. What is the missing factor of 36?

1, 2, 3, 4, 6, 9, ___, 18, 36

12. What is the sum of the four angles inside a rectangle?

13. What is the value of A?

27	24	39
		A
21	36	

14. What is the value of A?

33	21	
	27	A
	33	

15. What number is missing?   1, 3, 2, 6, ___, 9, 4

Answers

1.
2.
3.
4.
5.
6.
7.
8.
9.
10.
11.
12.
13.
14.
15.

One-a-Week Maths Tests: Age 10–11

Answers

Test 1
1. $\frac{7}{10}$
2. 5
3. no
4. 150
5. 150
6. d
7. 1000
8. 168 hours
9. 0.01
10. 75
11. 18
12. 6
13. d
14. 5
15. 13

Test 2
1. 7
2. 1025
3. 3.0
4. 31
5. horizontal
6. 15
7. 5
8. 10 days, 3 hours
9. 0.75
10. 1.67
11. 12
12. 36
13. c, d
14. a
15. 71

Test 3
1. 1, 2, 4, 5, 10, 20
2. 27
3. 3600
4. 16
5. 7.5
6. Friday
7. 8
8. 810
9. 0.05
10. 1.75
11. 26
12. $\frac{1}{2}$
13. 21
14. 36
15. 1642

Test 4
1. 1, 2, 3, 4, 6, 8, 12, 16, 24, 48
2. 1440
3. 24
4. 5
5. 10
6. reflex
7. 31.12.96
8. 2, 4, 8
9. $\frac{10}{100}$
10. 9990
11. $\frac{11}{100}$
12. 12
13. d
14. b
15. 28

Test 5
1. 1.95
2. Nancy
3. $\frac{1}{16}$
4. 162
5. 3
6. 13
7. 22
8. 18
9. 108
10. 15
11. $\frac{1}{2}$
12. yes
13. 2
14. 180°
15. 250

Test 6
1. 9.55
2. E, H
3. 8
4. Carol
5. 45
6. 9.00am
7. 828
8. 51
9. $\frac{8}{10}$ (8 tenths)
10. 1.8
11. 9
12. 15
13. 5 : 3
14. 6 : 7
15. 2 : 3

Test 7
1. $\frac{16}{36}$
2. :::::
3. 25
4. 3 : 4
5. 3
6. 15
7. 13
8. 0.09
9. 1.45
10. $\frac{1}{6}$
11. 135°
12. 8
13. a
14. a
15. 1915

Test 8
1. 326
2. 5 : 3
3. 8.19, 8.2, 8 $\frac{1}{4}$
4. 180 r 3
5. 8 : 16 (1 : 2)
6. 80
7. 37.68
8. 60°
9. 275.0
10. $\frac{8}{1000}$ (eight thousandths)
11. 21
12. 92 days
13. 11.15pm
14. 1.16pm
15. 35

Test 9
1. 8
2. 4
3. $\frac{12}{100}$, 1.1, $\frac{12}{10}$
4. 3
5. perpendicular
6. 8.59am
7. $\frac{2}{3}$
8. 45°
9. 727
10. 1277.5
11. 3
12. 132
13. 37 $\frac{1}{2}$ hr
14. 16, 36
15. 3.09, 3 $\frac{1}{2}$, 3.88

Test 10
1. 185
2. 46
3. 19.32
4. 297 000
5. 3 $\frac{3}{4}$ hr
6. 49
7. 4 : 3
8. 4
9. 8 $\frac{3}{4}$
10. 658
11. 8
12. 30
13. 12
14. 71
15. 9

Answers

Test 11
1. 1, 13
2. 5
3. 23
4. $\frac{1}{4}$
5. 1
6. 6, 10
7. 5
8. 240
9. $\frac{6}{1000}$
10. 150.00
11. 2
12. 21.63
13. 9
14. 12
15. $\frac{1}{4}$

Test 12
1. 36
2. 270°
3. no
4. 36
5. 35
6. even
7. 14
8. 23
9. 0.85
10. 42
11. 177
12. 15
13. 360°
14. 330
15. 43

Test 13
1. $\frac{3}{8}$
2. 1 000 000
3. $\frac{6}{10}$
4. 4006
5. 1
6. c
7. 25
8. 218 r 7
9. 36
10. 7
11. 2007
12. 30
13. 36
14. 8.50am
15. 49

Test 14
1. 4
2. 25
3. 64
4. 7
5. 31
6. 12
7. 1
8. 213 r 2
9. $\frac{1}{27}$
10. 90°
11. 24 − 8
12. 12
13. 45 hours
14. Thursday
15. 1.25

Test 15
1. 81
2. $\frac{1}{6}$
3. 510 r 10
4. 11.1
5. 7.00am
6. 2
7. 10
8. 2.8
9. 6
10. $\frac{1}{4}$
11. 12
12. 12
13. 15, 10
14. south
15. 300

Test 16
1. 21st
2. 15
3. 260 r 6
4. $\frac{1}{10\,000}$
5. 81
6. 900
7. August 1982
8. 7
9. 5
10. 2
11. 131.6
12. 144
13. north
14. 998
15. 408

Test 17
1. 0.01
2. A:20, B:70
3. $\frac{1}{100}$
4. $\frac{20}{4}$
5. diameter
6. 769
7. 27 : 33
8. 358 r 3
9. 9.6
10. $\frac{33}{24}$ ($1\frac{9}{24}$,$1\frac{3}{8}$)
11. 100
12. 2418
13. 3.50pm
14. A:13, B:9
15. 24

Test 18
1. 0.25
2. 9:31
3. 169
4. 9
5. $\frac{5}{8}$
6. west
7. 109
8. 584 r 9
9. 1000
10. 25%
11. 2
12. 4
13. 5
14. radius
15. $\frac{5}{12}$

Test 19
1. 5
2. 8
3. 1
4. 63, 84
5. 121
6. c
7. 3.768
8. 148
9. 290
10. 0.007
11. 75%
12. 147 r 3
13. A:19, B:16
14. 2.04, 2.048, 2.39
15. 10 to 2 (1.50)

Test 20
1. 90
2. even
3. 20
4. no
5. 28%
6. 30
7. 225
8. 122 r 13
9. 900
10. 10%
11. 2.199, 2.2, 2.22
12. 340
13. d
14. 24, 36
15. 25

Answers

Test 21

1.	0.1
2.	33
3.	153
4.	12, 18
5.	4
6.	Friday
7.	64
8.	314
9.	90%
10.	6
11.	1.019, 1.02, 1.19
12.	$\frac{1}{2}$
13.	10
14.	rectangle
15.	1

Test 22

1.	4.5
2.	20
3.	343
4.	200
5.	120°
6.	A:30, B:18
7.	no
8.	320
9.	12
10.	2
11.	150°
12.	2
13.	125
14.	Saturday
15.	184

Test 23

1.	25%
2.	71
3.	8991
4.	2
5.	60°
6.	3
7.	448
8.	190
9.	689 000
10.	20
11.	0.4
12.	125
13.	49%
14.	A:13, B:19
15.	36

Test 24

1.	4160
2.	1.009, 1.01, 1.011
3.	2
4.	$\frac{3}{4}$
5.	90°
6.	26
7.	$\frac{1}{3}$
8.	500 000
9.	10 000
10.	45°
11.	$\frac{2}{5}$
12.	157
13.	60°
14.	60°
15.	28, 56

Test 25

1.	0.03
2.	70°
3.	382
4.	$\frac{1}{5}$
5.	95
6.	4°
7.	3
8.	1
9.	80
10.	146 r 8
11.	50
12.	24, 48
13.	c
14.	7°
15.	60

Test 26

1.	400 000
2.	3
3.	6
4.	54
5.	216
6.	640
7.	186 r 7
8.	−5°C
9.	1
10.	100
11.	2197
12.	E, H, M, Z
13.	28
14.	140
15.	120

Test 27

1.	559
2.	36
3.	30
4.	262.5
5.	48
6.	320°
7.	16
8.	40
9.	52
10.	0
11.	614 r 7
12.	24
13.	30
14.	12
15.	43

Test 28

1.	26
2.	301
3.	100
4.	2°C
5.	pentagon
6.	60°
7.	6
8.	70%
9.	4
10.	3.0
11.	324
12.	24
13.	11%
14.	$\frac{1}{5}$
15.	c

Test 29

1.	810
2.	135°
3.	16
4.	80%
5.	36
6.	100°
7.	100
8.	393 r 12
9.	441
10.	1728
11.	$\frac{1}{32}$
12.	11
13.	75°
14.	12
15.	hexagon

Test 30

1.	$\frac{3}{8}$
2.	180
3.	−9, −8, −7, −6
4.	36, 49
5.	40°
6.	6
7.	16
8.	4
9.	72
10.	3
11.	4
12.	130 r 19
13.	d
14.	55°
15.	11

Answers

Test 31

1.	400 r 1
2.	7
3.	7471
4.	−11, −5, 0, 4
5.	108
6.	120°
7.	60°
8.	$\frac{9}{100}$, $\frac{1}{10}$, 11%
9.	19
10.	$\frac{7}{20}$
11.	80
12.	27
13.	A:18, B:24
14.	$\frac{1}{6}$
15.	3.40

Test 32

1.	no
2.	81
3.	1.25
4.	4
5.	200
6.	60°
7.	180
8.	558 r 4
9.	39
10.	$\frac{4}{25}$
11.	20:00
12.	1825.0
13.	$\frac{1}{10}$
14.	6
15.	17

Test 33

1.	15:15
2.	75%
3.	+1
4.	7
5.	19
6.	90°
7.	3000
8.	36
9.	91 r 5
10.	1296
11.	11.08pm
12.	$\frac{1}{3}$
13.	28
14.	29°
15.	13

Test 34

1.	812
2.	31
3.	4096
4.	5
5.	9792
6.	15
7.	0.95sec
8.	quadrilateral
9.	6561
10.	$6\frac{1}{2}$
11.	3
12.	18
13.	553
14.	80°
15.	220

Test 35

1.	244
2.	32
3.	$\frac{5}{6}$
4.	−2
5.	624
6.	70°
7.	29
8.	00:01
9.	243
10.	8
11.	−2
12.	56
13.	10
14.	55°
15.	360 times

Test 36

1.	12
2.	5
3.	23:59
4.	60°
5.	9.45
6.	145°
7.	1519
8.	$\frac{1}{8}$
9.	10, 12
10.	3
11.	6
12.	1024
13.	c
14.	8
15.	9

Test 37

1.	269
2.	60°
3.	114
4.	09:28
5.	56
6.	64
7.	4
8.	circle
9.	450°
10.	−2
11.	23:36
12.	18, 22
13.	135°
14.	45°
15.	520

Test 38

1.	729
2.	6
3.	21
4.	12
5.	7yr 6mth
6.	30°
7.	40
8.	26
9.	350
10.	24
11.	319 r 1
12.	2
13.	6
14.	30
15.	10

Test 39

1.	4
2.	132
3.	16:40
4.	2 : 3
5.	150°
6.	1.6
7.	1597°C
8.	00:00
9.	1.0
10.	128
11.	125 000
12.	12
13.	10
14.	135°
15.	30

Test 40

1.	10
2.	36, 44
3.	1
4.	−1
5.	7.12pm
6.	135°
7.	75°
8.	256
9.	2.2
10.	9
11.	12
12.	360°
13.	18
14.	33
15.	3